Star Learning Diploma
5-7 years

Phonics

**Illustrated by
Heather Heyworth**

Autumn
Publishing

Say the sound

Draw a circle around the picture in each row that starts with the
same sound as the letter. Be careful, sometimes there are two!

l

n

d

k

f

q

Well done! Give yourself
a gold tick.

Now stick a gold star on
your diploma.

j

p

v

w

x

y

z

Well done! Give yourself
a gold tick.

Now stick a gold star on
your diploma.

Write the first letter

Look at the pictures. The first sound in each word is missing.
Can you say the sound and write the missing letter?

_nchor

_all

_ar

_uck

_lephant

_ish

_ate

_at

_gloo

_ellyfish

_angaroo

_ion

_oon

_urse

_range

_anda

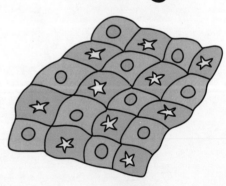

_uilt

_abbit

_ock

_able

_mbrella

_ase

_atch

_-ray

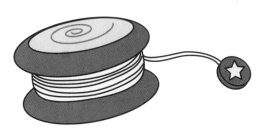

_o-yo

_ebra

Well done! Give yourself
a gold tick.

Now stick a gold star on
your diploma.

Listen for the last sound

Say the sound of each letter. Then say the word in each picture,
listening carefully for the final sound in the word.
Join the letters to the pictures that end with the same sound.

Excellent!
Now stick a gold
star on
your diploma.

Write the last letter

Look at the pictures. The last sound in each word is missing.
Can you say the sound and write the missing letter?

we_

su_

ca_

fo_

mo_

Well done! Give yourself
a gold tick.

Now stick a gold star on
your diploma.

he_

ba_

bu_

sta_

boo_

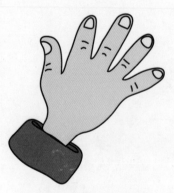

han_

gir_

bo_

6

si_

lea_

bo_

clou_

Well done! Give yourself
a gold tick.

Now stick a gold star on
your diploma.

Sounds in the middle

The letters **a**, **e**, **i**, **o** and **u** are called **vowels**.
Look at the pictures. The vowel sound in the middle of each word is missing.
Can you say the missing vowel sound and write the letter?

c_p

c_p

h_t

h_t

p_n

m_p

m_p

m_t

c_t

b_ll   l_g   p_g

s_n   f_n   b_ll

b_x   d_g   f_n

b_s

Well done! Give yourself a gold tick.

Now stick a gold star on your diploma.

Middle double letters

Double letter sounds can be in the middle of words.
Look at the pictures and write the missing letters.

r_ _ t

g_ _ se

bu_ _ on

sh_ _ p

ca_ _ ot

sp_ _ n

b_ _ k

Excellent!
Now stick a gold
star on
your diploma.

Write the words

Look at the pictures and say the words. Find the words in the box
and write the missing letters. Draw lines to join the words and pictures.

hi_ _

tr_ _

kangar_ _

she_ _

dre_ _

be_ _

Well done! Give yourself
a gold tick.

Now stick a gold star on
your diploma.

Double letters at the end

Some words have double letters at the end. Look at the pictures,
say the word and write the missing letters.

wa_ _

ba_ _

we_ _

gla_ _

b_ _

z_ _

Excellent!
Now stick a gold
star on
your diploma.

More double letters!

Look at the pictures and write the missing double letters.
Which word on this page has two sets of double letters?

pu_ _y

pa_ _ot

b_ _t

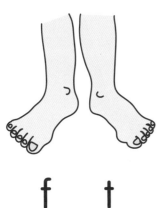

f_ _t

ball_ _n

m_ _n

ki_ _ _en

g_ _se

Well done! Give yourself
a gold tick.

Now stick a gold star on
your diploma.

Rhyming sounds

When two words sound the similar, they **rhyme**.
Look at the pictures in each set of rhyming words.
Write the first letter sounds in each word.

_at

_at

_at

_an

_an

_an

_en

_en

_en

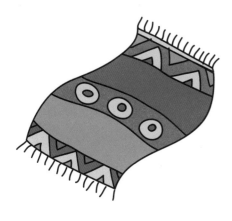

_ug

_ug

_ug

_ing

_ing

_ing

_ock

_lock

Well done! Give yourself a gold tick.

Now stick a gold star on your diploma.

Rhyming words

Say the words for each picture and join the two words that rhyme.
Underline the rhyming words in each box.

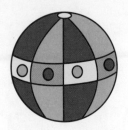

ball
butterfly
wall
flower
chair

mat
book
vase
cat
apple

pear
hat
fish
dish
book

mitten
ladder
scissors
kitten
clock

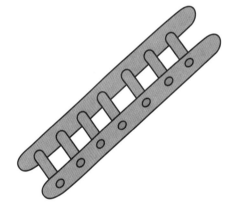

Well done! Give yourself
a gold tick.

Now stick a gold star on
your diploma.

First and last

The first and last letters in each word are missing.
Write the letters to complete the words.

_oo_

_ir_

low

_oa_

_o_

_ta_

_oo_

_uc_

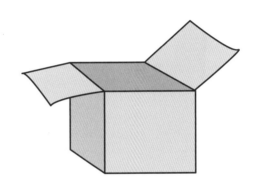

_o_

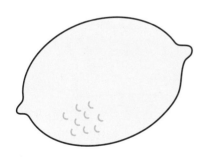

emo

Well done! Give yourself a gold tick.

Now stick a gold star on your diploma.

Letter e at the end

The letter **e** at the end of a word changes the vowel sound in the word.
Look at the example then add an **e** to the words.

pin

pine
_____

cap

_____

man

_____

cub

Excellent!
Now stick a gold
star on
your diploma.

_____

Take off the e

Now take off the **e** to make new words.

tube

_____

rate

_____

hate

_____

pane

_____

fine

_____

Well done! Give yourself
a gold tick.

Now stick a gold star on
your diploma.

Sound patterns

Sometimes we join two letter sounds together to make a new sound.
Write the letters to complete the words.

l__f   p___ch   ___gle

h__se   cl__d   f__ntain

cl__n

t__el

sh__er

tr__n

p__nt

sn__l

b__t

g__t

Well done! Give yourself a gold tick.

Now stick a gold star on your diploma.

Sounds the same

Look at each picture and say the word underneath. Now find a word in the box that sounds exactly the same but is spelled differently. Join the words together with a line.

bear

hare

plane

pear

eight

write

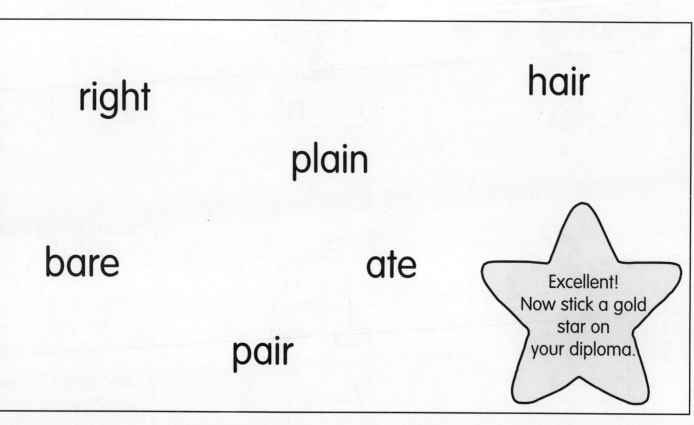

right

hair

plain

bare

ate

pair

Excellent! Now stick a gold star on your diploma.

Different spellings

Look at the words in the boxes. Now look at the pictures and write
the words that sound the same but are spelled differently.
The first one has been done for you.

so

pair

sew

_____

ate

see

_____

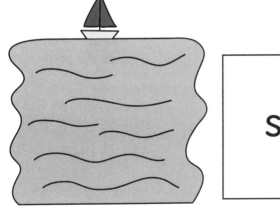

_____

Well done! Give yourself
a gold tick.

Now stick a gold star on
your diploma.

Answers

Say the sound
snail and sun
moon
cat
triangle and tortoise
goat and gate
hat
lamb
nose and net
dolphin and dog
kite
fork and fish
queen
ant
egg
ink and igloo
octopus
umbrella
ball and baby
rake and ring
jam
pan
violin
watch and window
x-ray
yo-yo
zebra

Write the first letter
anchor
ball
car
duck
elephant
fish
gate
hat
igloo
jellyfish
kangaroo
lion
moon
nurse
orange
panda
quilt
rabbit
sock
table
umbrella
vase
watch
x-ray
yo-yo
zebra

Listen for the last sound
arm
hat and boat
cup
box and six

Write the last letter
web
sum
cat
fox
mop
hen
bag
bus
star
book
hand
girl
boy
six
leaf
cloud
bow

Sounds in the middle
cap
cup
hat
hut
pen
map
mop
mat
cat
bell
leg
pig
sun
fan
ball
box
dog
fin
bus

Middle double letters
root
geese
button
sheep
carrot
spoon
book

Write the words
hill
tree
kangaroo
shell
dress
bell

Double letters at the end
wall
ball
well
glass
bee
zoo

More double letters!
puppy
parrot
boot
feet
balloon
moon
kitten
goose
'balloon' has two sets of double letters.

Rhyming sounds
bat
hat
rat
van
man
fan
hen
pen
ten
rug
hug
mug
ring
king
wing
rock
clock

Rhyming words
ball and wall
mat and cat
fish and dish
kitten and mitten

First and last
moon
bird
clown
boat
fox
star
book
duck
box
lemon

Letter e at the end
cape
mane
cube

Take off the e
tub
rat
hat
pan
fin

Sound patterns
leaf
peach
eagle
house
cloud
fountain
clown
towel
shower
train
paint
snail
boat
goat

Sounds the same
bear and bare
hare and hair
plane and plain
pear and pair
eight and ate
write and right

Different spellings
pear
sea
eight